WOODLAND CREATURES
NIGHT & DAY
COLOURING BOOK

THIS IS A CARLTON BOOK

Published by Carlton Books Ltd
20 Mortimer Street
London W1T 3JW

Copyright © 2016 Carlton Books Ltd

A CIP catalogue record for this book is available from the British Library

10 9 8 7 6 5 4 3 2

ISBN 978-1-78097-859-8

Printed in China

WOODLAND CREATURES

NIGHT & DAY

COLOURING BOOK

ILLUSTRATED BY PATRICIA MOFFETT

CARLTON BOOKS

CONTENTS

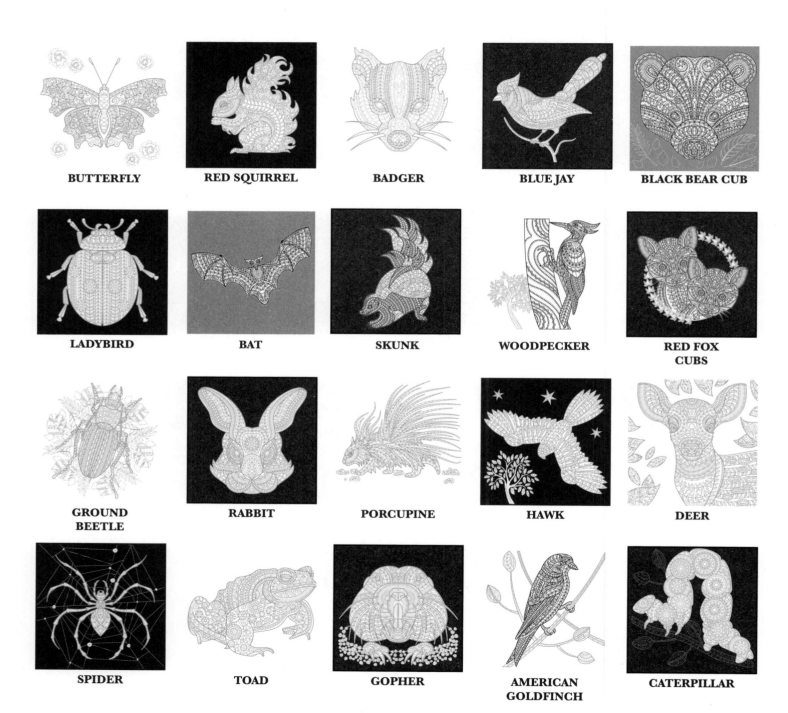

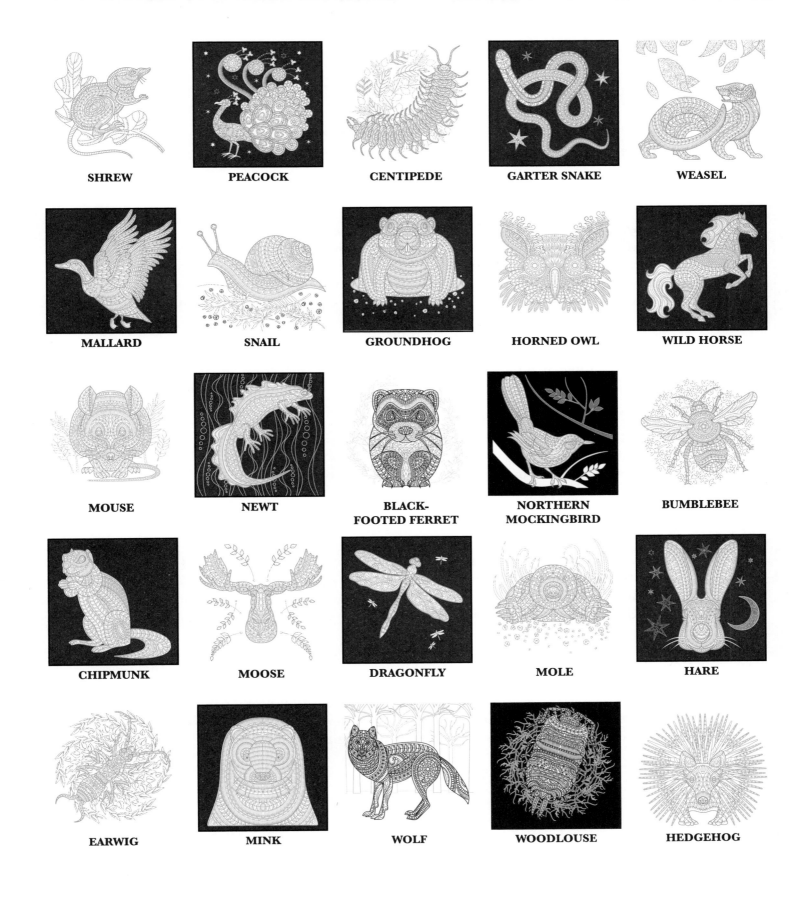

SHREW

PEACOCK

CENTIPEDE

GARTER SNAKE

WEASEL

MALLARD

SNAIL

GROUNDHOG

HORNED OWL

WILD HORSE

MOUSE

NEWT

BLACK-
FOOTED FERRET

NORTHERN
MOCKINGBIRD

BUMBLEBEE

CHIPMUNK

MOOSE

DRAGONFLY

MOLE

HARE

EARWIG

MINK

WOLF

WOODLOUSE

HEDGEHOG

Introduction

Welcome to a new colouring challenge!

The *Woodland Creatures Night & Day Colouring Book* is unique because it invites you to colour not just against white, but also blue, black and gold backgrounds. Each of the 90 detailed outlines featured here are displayed against both a day and a night backdrop, providing you with superb opportunities to highlight tone and texture, and create striking contrasts.

While daylight can illuminate subtle motifs and tints, darkness can bring out flashes of colour or the sparkle of eyes and teeth. In fact, you'll find there's a surprising difference between a creature depicted in golden sunshine or azure seas and that same creature shown against a background of inky darkness or deep waters.

The woodland creatures presented in this book range from huge animals to tiny insects. They include many favourites, such as the butterfly, hedgehog, peacock, and black bear cub, as well as less familiar creatures, like the black-footed ferret, groundhog, porcupine and mink. There are intricately patterned creatures, such as the snail and garter snake, and nocturnal animals, including the mouse, badger and horned owl.

What was beautiful in the daytime can seem threatening at night, and what was subtle in the light can emerge from darkness as striking or even eerie. How will your daylight hawk differ from your midnight version? Could your drowsy daytime red fox cubs become moonlight predators? Might the blue jay's pretty colours turn neon after dark?

How you decide to bring out the appearance, character and qualities of each beast is determined by you and the colour choices you make on each artwork. You can be as accurate and realistic, or as creative and fantasy-filled, as you like. Working with the coloured backgrounds opens up exciting possibilities and an invigorating new world of colouring, so let your imagination – and your pens – run wild.

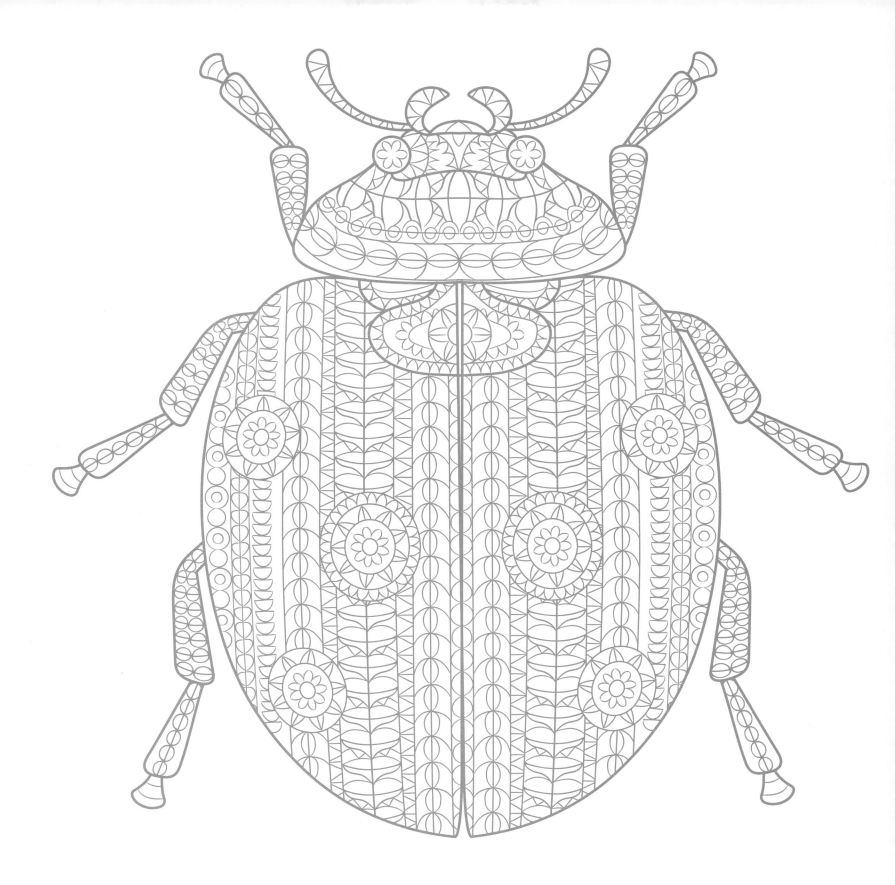

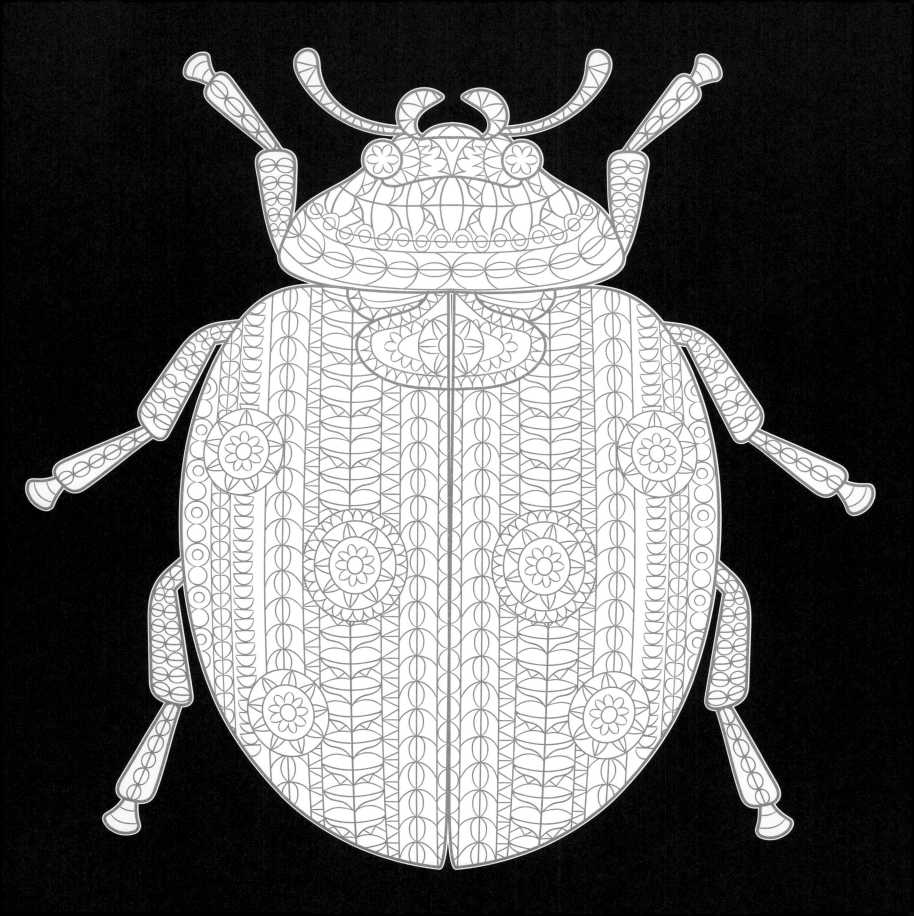

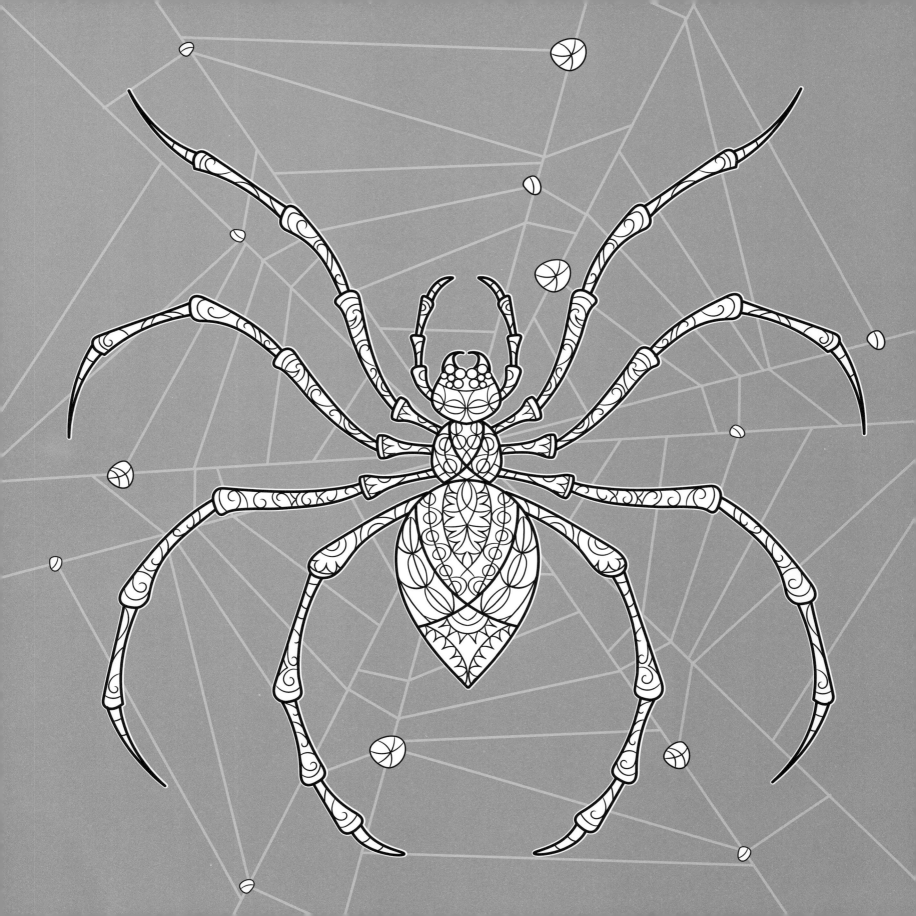

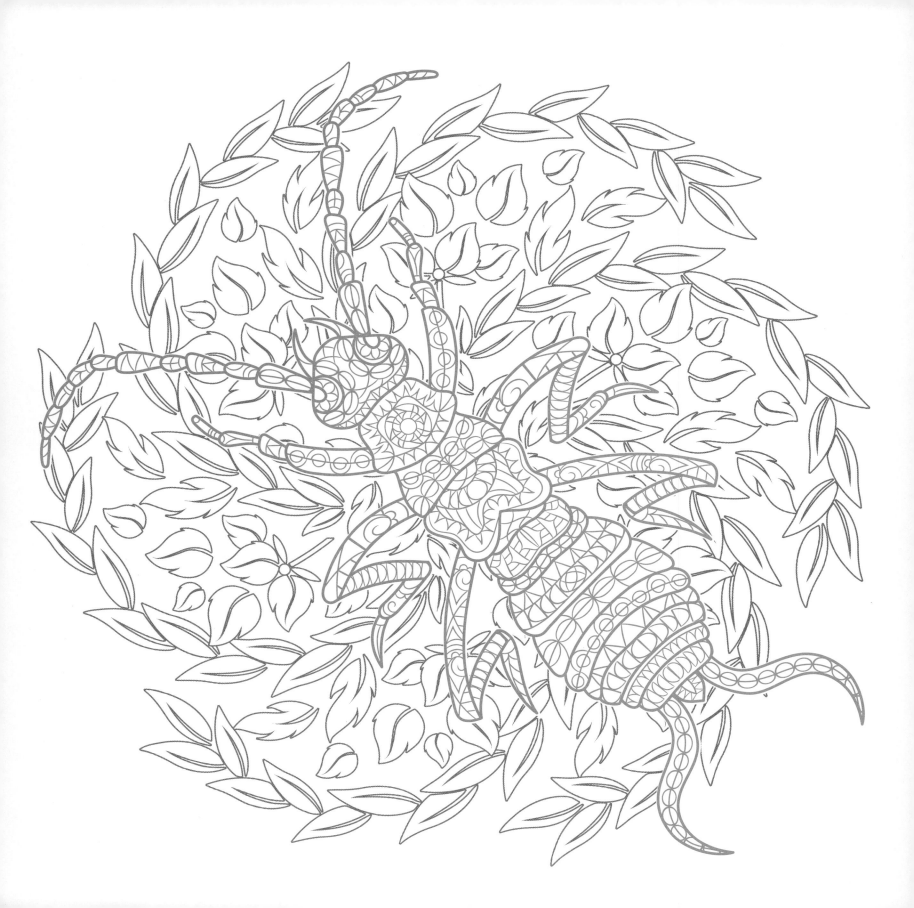

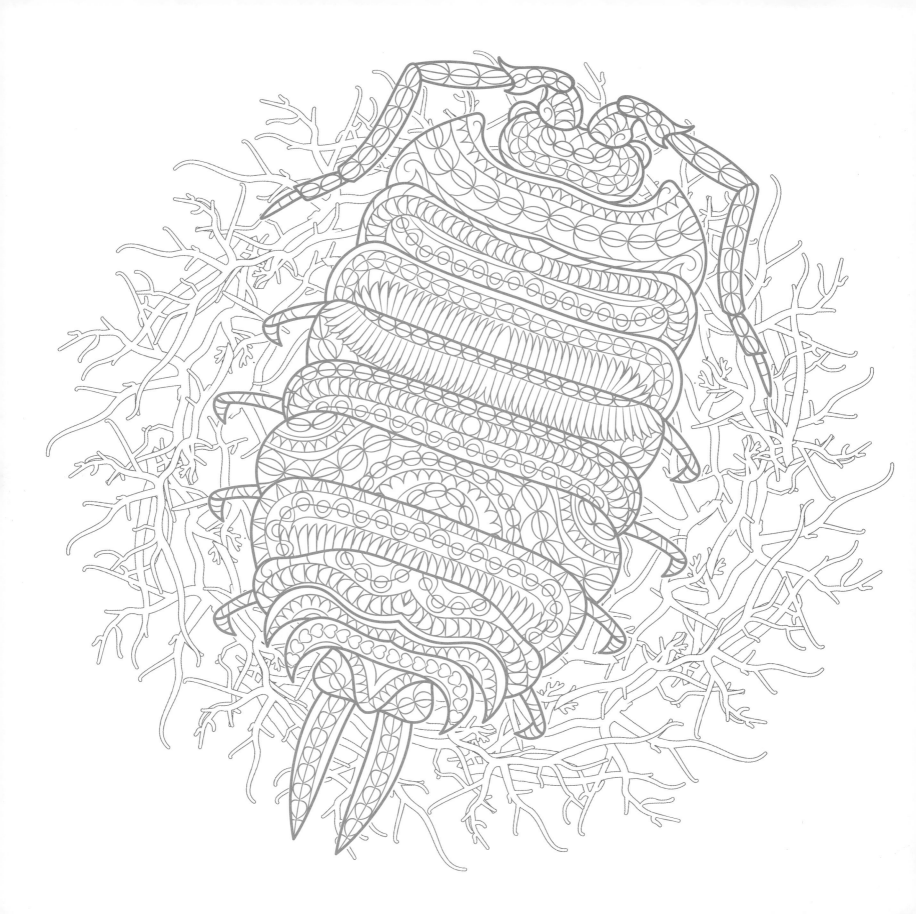

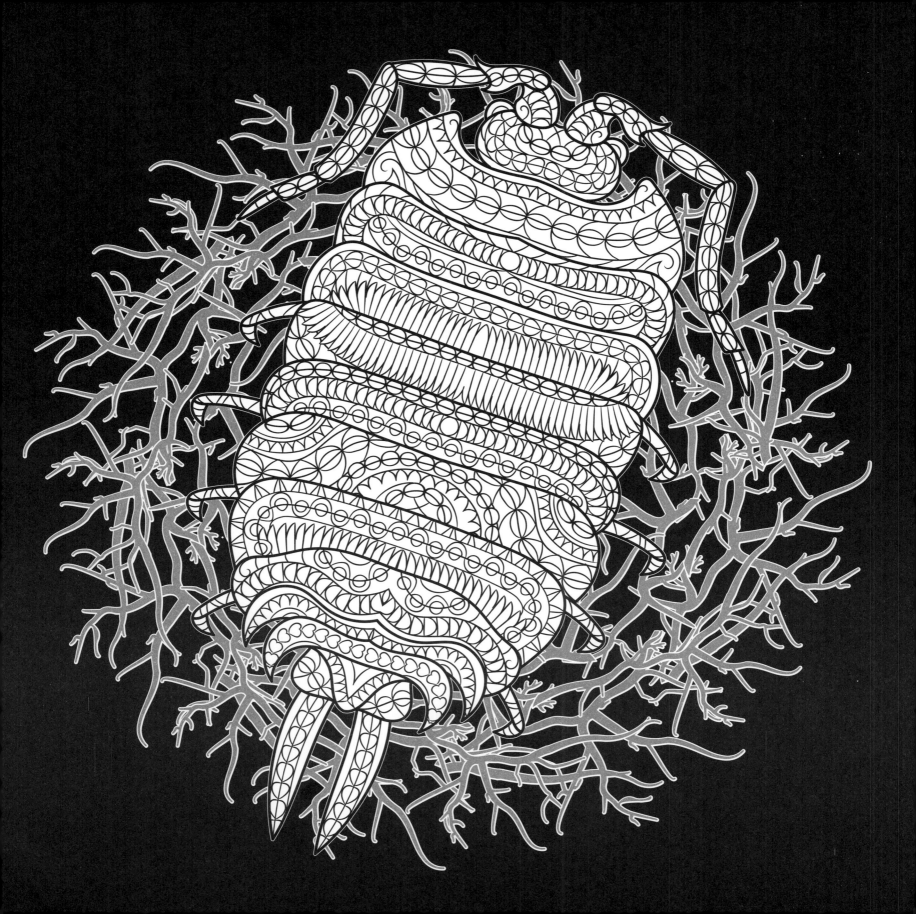